Hanley Wakes

Hanley Wakes

By Derrick Woodward

TCP BOOKS

Three Counties Publishing (Books) Limited

Hanley Wakes

Published by

Three Counties Publishing (Books) Limited

P.O. Box 435 Leek, Staffordshire England, ST13 5TB
telephone 01538 380910 fax 01538 382204

© Derrick Woodward and
TCP (Books) Limited 2002

ISBN 0 - 95352398 - 8 - 5

Typeset by Clerment Ferrand International, Staffordshire, England, ST13 5TB
and Printed by J. H. Brookes (Printers) Ltd, Stoke on Trent, England

Hanley Wakes - Memories of a childhood in the Potteries

A Half-crown to spend at Pat Collin's fair in Regent Road – Hanley Wakes, a visit to the Saturday morning matinee at the local cinema, an outing to the Theatre Royal to perch high in the 'gods' for the Christmas panto, those were high spots of the year for the average child in Hanley during the 1940's

Growing up in a town which had scarcely changed in a century, where dark back entries and derelict buildings were commonplace, we roamed the streets in safety and made our own entertainment. Swimming in the River Trent, sledging on the Aerial dirt tip at Hanley Deep Pit, camping with the Scouts. Playing Hopscotch, tick, top and whip, marbles and Rally an' Go, we relished our freedom and the long summer evenings.

Different times, different ways, but we enjoyed our childhood then, and this book attempts to relive those days.

Foreword

What memories this book brings back to me! Shops, churches, entertainment to suit adults and children, and many other things as they used to be. Has Hanley changed for the better? Maybe in some ways it has, but to me it is a different town altogether, so it would be a great pity if things which once gave Hanley a character of its own are forgotten-things like the hot potato stall, the Salvation Army marching to the Citadel from the Market Square, the Markets, Pat Collins' Wakes and many others.

The author of this book gives a detailed and fascinating word-picture of old Hanley and the ways in which people who lived there spent their time.

This book deserves to be widely read and preserved in the City archives for future generations to read.

Mrs. Nora Landon B.E.M

Hanley Wakes

Acknowledgements

My grateful thanks to all those who have contributed to this book in so many ways.

Mrs. Nora Landon B.E.M. kindly provided the foreword and introduced members of the King George the Sixth Club, who supplied the photographs on pages 20 to 24 inclusive,33, 34, 42, 58, 73, 79, 81 and 82.

The Potteries Museum and Art Gallery for permission to use photographs on pages 25, 37, 61, 62, 78

Pictures of old Hanley Market Square kindly loaned by the Lewis's Ice Cream manufacturers appear on Pages 29 and 39.

Wartime original photos on pages 18 and 69 appear by kind permission of Mr. & Mrs. E. Johnston and Mr. E. Wright respectively.

Illustrations and photographs on the following pages have been donated anonymously: 13, 14, 15, 19, 44, 83 and 84.

The remaining photographs used in this book are either in the authors collection or have been taken by the author.

The author and publisher have tried to identify and acknowledge all photographs or illustrations used within this book and wish to apologise should any acknowledgement have been omitted due to the inability to identify the owner.

Preface

Hanley Wakes

. . . . .is fiction, but fiction based on the memories of a generation who remember Hanley as it used to be, half a lifetime ago. Much of the material in this book comes from Potters encountered whilst writing a weekly local interest column, the remainder from old memories shared, scrapbooks and letters.

Recalling Hanley illuminated by gaslight, the 'monkey run' courtship ritual in Hope Street and the cockloft in the old market. The 'Ideal' and the 'Majestic', the 'Roxy' and the 'Empire', where have they gone - and where have the years gone?

Wherever they've passed, they were happier times and those who remember were more contented people – *Happy Days!*

Hanley Wakes is dedicated to my dear parents, William and Gladys, to my family today, to my siblings and to old schoolmates.

Derrick Woodward

Contents

You can order further copies of this book and other books by
Three Counties Publishing (Books) Ltd.
by filling in and returning the order form on page 95

Hanley Wakes

Chapter One

'Holidays at Home'

Holidays at home were the order of the day for the Potteries and the rest of the United Kingdom immediately following the 1939 - 45 World War. All consumer goods, including petrol, were strictly rationed and the old wartime slogan "is your journey really necessary?" still applied. When the local factories closed for the annual Wakes holidays during the first two weeks in August and the customary pall of smoke from the coal fired bottle ovens lifted for a while, many holidaymakers looked to Hanley Park for their recreation.

The parks had hosted many fetes and celebrations during the war years, fighter planes had been displayed to help the Spitfire Fund raise more cash to help build these famous aircraft, which had been designed in the City.

The pipes and drums of the Scottish Regiment take their place in the march through Festival Park,

Parades by the Services took place in many of the City parks, including spectacular appearances by the full dress marching bands of many units. The Drum and Bugle Corp. of the Fijian police are shown leading one such parade, followed by the pipes and drums of

The Mounted Drum and Bugle Corps of a Portugese unit follow on, sabres and sunglasses are the order of the day

Dressed in full ceremonial uniform, the band of the Fijian Police join the opening ceremony at Hanley Garden Festival

A Drum Major and Bandmaster lead the Band of the Royal Air Force
in a parade through Hanley's Garden Festival

Crack troops of the Cavalry Regiment form the rear guard during the
opening ceremony for Festival Park

an Highland Regiment, the Central Band of the R.A.F, a unit including a mounted drum major wearing resplendent plumed helmets
and the hussars, with sabres drawn, riding magnificent bays. With
bonfires and firework displays to commemorate V.EDay (Victory in
Europe) and V. J Day (Victory over Japan), which had taken place in
Hanley Park, famed for pre-war fetes and firework displays.

Now that peace had finally arrived people could watch their children playing in the sandpit by the paddock, fish, boat or feed the birds on the lake. The bandstand, where military bands played popular tunes attracted many spectators, while the bowling greens and the park pavilion were always popular.

In the lower park, the huge Victorian glasshouses had been cleared of the remnants of the 'Dig for Victory' campaign of the wartime years and were returning to their former glory with a display of tropical plants, orchids and palms. Also on this section of the park, the ornamental red brick and tile fountain had been restored to full working order, sending sprays of water cascading onto the formal flower display at its base.

Unlike many other parks, Hanley park had not lost the ornamental iron railings and gates to the wartime scrap collectors, when so many were melted down for munitions. There was a recreation ground at Sneyd Green, which was known to schoolchildren as the 'Wreck'. Each school sports day we would form up crocodile fashion, wearing sashes of coloured cloth to denote the different teams and march to this sports field, which had one feature which always amused us.

Just prior to the war, King George the sixth had ceremonially opened the grounds, which were enclosed by wrought iron railings and a set of suitably inscribed gates commemorating the event. In common with many others, the railings were removed as scrap metal to aid the war effort, but the gates remained firmly in place. Every morning and evening a park keeper would ensure that the gates were locked and unlocked, although nothing else obstructed entrance!

We would mark out lanes on the red ash surface with lime and take our places for the games, featuring such athletic events as the egg and spoon race, with a potato substituting for the egg, due to rationing. The slow bike race was another popular spectacle, the last to cross the finishing line was the winner and there were some nasty spills as the riders wobbled down the pitch. The mothers' race was always keenly contested as the first prize was a large bunch of flowers grown on the nearby school allotment. Our mum won this event once, borrowing someone's pumps as plimsolls were known before designer trainers arrived. She was delighted with her trophy, remarking that the flowers would be ideal to place on Nan's grave in 'Kent's Garden' as the cemetery was always known.

Another exciting run was the paperchase, one boy would be adorned with a newspaper satchel full of scrap paper and given five minutes start to lay a trail up Birches Head Lane, around the duck pond in the farmyard next to the vicarage and return to the sports field through the allotments. This race ended suddenly once, after a thunderstorm puddled the allotment paths and one boy who was wearing wellies decided to run through a puddle. It turned out to be a shallow well serving the allotments and he disappeared neck deep!

Sports day over we made our way home, munching a stick of rhubarb or a 'shonnock', a swede pulled from the allotments. Our way led by Alderman Barkers' Birches Head home, seen in the photo on the next page, being presented with a contribution to the Spitfire fund by a group of our schoolmates, including Jean Macvitie, who is handing over a wad of the old big, treasury notes, Marjorie Wardle, Rosie Nixon and Albert Shenton standing by Alderman Barker. The youngster on the left is Ernie Johnston, who kindly contributed this picture.

One of the most popular attractions during the holidays, which drew visitors from all over Stoke on Trent, was the travelling funfair, known as Pat Collins' Wakes, which visited Hanley during the first two weeks of August. A complete carnival would be set up on the site of a marl hole, just off Regent Road in Hanley, normally used as a 'shord-ruck', or a dump for faulty pottery.

On the Sunday before the wakes, a procession of caravans, dismantled rides and fittings, would arrive in town and by August Bank Holiday Monday the fair would be ready for business. Dominating the scene would be the Big Wheel, a huge ferris wheel which adjoined the helter-skelter, always a popular viewpoint to see all the fun of the fair.

There was a ride called the Chair-o-planes, resembling a spinning top with swings suspended by chains from the top. As this ride gathered speed, the swings would rise almost horizontally, giving the riders the choice of hanging onto the safety chain or their valuables.

The Cake Walk was another well patronised ride consisting of a long walkway with handrails, which shook and vibrated as the customers tried to walk along it. A queue always formed for the bumping cars or dodgems, there was great demand for the fastest or the flashiest ones with the shiniest chrome and patrons would run across the floor to grab one almost before the ride stopped. These cars were electrically driven, rather like tramcars with a long rod at the rear to conduct a charge from the wire mesh roofing to

the drive wheels. A strong smell of ozone filled the air around this ride, as sparks flew all ways.

Then there were the Waltzers, circular cars, seating half a dozen people, which spun on their axis as they progressed around a circular track.

The Grand National completed the larger rides, this was an affair of gaily painted horses, all in authentic racing colours of the day, which rose and fell realistically as they galloped on an undulating track to the cheers of the spectators. Beside the track stood a Tote board, where bets could be placed using tokens purchased from a small booth. Winning punters were paid out with a packet of sweets or a free ride.

Minor attractions, costing a copper a go included a miniature Las Vegas which featured scores of one armed bandits, (slot machines to us) including mini cranes in cases which punters controlled to try and grab a prize. Coconut shies and hoopla stalls stood beside booths inviting fairgoers to try and hook a plastic duck from a number bobbing in a water trough, with the chance to win a prize if the captured duck bore a lucky number.

There were freak shows and boxing booths, try your strength machines where customers swung a mallet to try and ring the bell, the Ghost Train to scare the kids and lots of roundabouts, with anything from swans to the kiddycars shown here.

Then when darkness fell, the Wakes ground took on a magical atmosphere,

the bright lights attracted the older generation to hear the latest records, blaring at top volume from amplifiers far more powerful than the hand cranked gramophones in most homes.

Later in the evening, as the lights of the Wakes dimmed, the customers began making their way to Hanley town centre to seek other amusement.

Entertainment was plentiful and cheap in Hanley then, there were a multitude of pubs, a theatre and no fewer than six cinemas, the most popular family outing. These included the Roxy, in Glass Street, which had a steep entrance ramp in Church Street and re-sounded to the thunder of feet as children charged in to watch the Saturday matinee, admission threepence. The matinee programme included a feature film, probably starring Gene Autry, Roy Rogers or Errol Flynn, a second feature which might be a Laurel and Hardy film, an Abbot and Costello comedy or include the Bowery Boys. With a cartoon, perhaps a Mickey Mouse or Donald Duck, Saturday morning soon passed. In addition to matinees, the Roxy changed programmes three times a week, with screenings from Monday to Wednesday, a different show on Thursday to Saturday and again on Sunday.

At sixpence a seat, this was real value for money and the double sofa seats in the balcony were an added attraction for courting couples.

The junction of Pall Mall and Picaddily. c.1947 on the left is the rear of what was then the Regent Cinema

Just around the corner in New Street, the Capitol had another childrens' matinee, including a club anthem 'minors of the A. B. C'. The projection equipment at the Capitol was being replaced and the screen here was at an acute angle, so the first few rows of the audience were practically lying in their seats with cricks in their necks. Mr. Radford, the manager at the Capitol was a great showman and for new British films like the 'Barretts of Wimpole Street' and 'The Dancing Years' he would take great pains to ensure the stage and proscenium

Seats available in all parts, as the Odeon Cinema finally closes, another victim of T.V. and Bingo

were decorated appropriately. Then there was the Palace, the largest cinema in the area, which stood opposite Hanley town hall in the position recently vacated by C&A. On a foggy winter night the cigarette smoke in the cinema could mingle with the fog to such an extent that the light from the projector hardly reached the screen.

The Empire cinema was long and narrow, extending from Piccadilly through to Trinity Street entering in Trinity Street, and leaving in Piccadilly. This site is now occupied by a shopping arcade. A peculiarity of the Empire was that some patrons in the stalls were unable to watch the action on the screen as their view was obscured by the pillars which supported the balcony!

A little further down Piccadilly stood the Regent (aka the Gaumont) a striking building which achieved Grade Two listed status as an example of the Art Deco school. The dome over the auditorium is particularly striking and used to house the film projectors. In 1947 and for some years thereafter, the Regent boasted a comfortable cafe where cinema patrons could enjoy a meal after the show, a dance studio was also accommodated in the same building.

On the corner of Trinity Street and Foundry Street the Odeon was erected, replacing the old Grand theatre which burned down some years previously. An impressive, comfortable cinema, it established records for exhibiting popular films, 'The Sound of Music' and 'South Pacific' were two which played to capacity audiences for many weeks.

In addition to these professional venues, church halls and youth clubs would hold film shows for a penny admission. I especially recall watching 'Hell's Angels' an exciting aerial film of WW1, at St. Luke's church hall. A popular feature of these shows would be a silent film, displaying the words of a current song. As a little white ball marked time over the words on the screen, it would be accom-

Beyond the St. John's Church the New Bank Buildings are nearing completion where the Ideal Skating Rink stood

panied by a pianist while the audience sang along - the forerunner of karaoke.

Other entertainments included the Ideal skating rink, which stood in Town Road on the site now occupied by Barclays bank. (photo. Church). This was a favourite with the airmen from the huge R. A. F base at Stafford, who travelled to Hanley to live it up on the twenty-eight shillings (£1.40) paid weekly to National servicemen in the days of conscription.

A regular trick with those young men was to coax a young girl, nervous on hired skates, into the middle of the rink holding both hands to help her balance. Having reached the middle they'd abandon her to await help of her friends. A disused graveyard adjoined the Ideal and was concealed by high brick walls providing perfect cover for courting couples.

A centuries old tomb in the overgrown graveyard behind the Ideal

Then there was the Theatre Royal, a real survivor of the Victorian music hall, which offered cheap and cheerful entertainment. A seat in the 'Gods' as the upper balcony was known, cost a few pence and from this steep perch a fine view was obtained of the whole theatre.

A bar opened before and after the show, also at the interval; right opposite the stage door stood the Mechanics pub, a cheerful, snug little place, patronised by many of the variety acts appearing at the theatre. Crowds used to gather outside the Mechanics, which provided a fine view of the stage door, autograph hunters waited there and when Tommy Steele appeared at the theatre one young girl climbed a drainpipe trying to reach his dressing room.

Opposite the front entrance to the Theatre Royal was the Majestic ballroom, with a billiard hall above. This billiard hall contained about a dozen full size tables and was always crowded, especially at weekends. One table stood in a raised alcove by the main window and was a popular choice, as it offered a good view of the dancers entering the main ballroom, giving the young men about town an opportunity to survey the 'talent' as they called the girls. A large revolving multifaceted glass ball dominated the ballroom and as this ball revolved, the spotlight trained on it cast reflections into every corner. There was a dais to one side where the band sat, croon- ers in the style of Bing Crosby were still popular then and one of the most fashionable dances was the jitterbug, bought over by the U. S.

An unusual view of Hanley showing the old Gas Offices, the American P.X. and traffic running into Market Square from Tontine Street.

Airforce, members of the 8th air arm who had been billeted in and around Hanley during the war. These American servicemen used the building which now houses the Halifax as their P. X or club and as sweets like everything else were rationed in 1947, we children used to greet the Yanks with the traditional cry "Got any gum, chum"?

We didn't always get a reward for our entreaties, but more often than not we'd be presented with some strange American candy, as they called what we knew as 'rock'. Babe Ruth chocolate, Hershey bars, lifesavers and Juicy Fruit chewing gum were all given freely, though sometimes the troops were more interested in enquiring if we had big sisters!

Wrestling was another crowd puller and was presented at the Victoria Hall on Saturday evenings, the Hall was used for many purposes then, some of us sat our eleven plus grammar school exams there, lots of scope to wander round and consult with our friends.

Apart from all this, free or inexpensive pastimes were plentiful in the Hanley of nineteen forty seven. The workingmen's club was in its heyday then, a typical one

Photograph courtesy of the Potteries Museum and Art Gallery

Remember this? Roast taters at threpence a bag, being sold outside the Wesminster Bank

being the Hanley Central Working-men's club, situated in Glass Street. In common with most clubs, this was run by a management committee and provided entertainment such as a singer, a comedian, a musical group or a similar act on a well appointed stage in comfortable surroundings. Bingo, dancing, members' outings and other social events featured on a regular basis, the kids weren't forgotten either, enjoying an annual outing, a Christmas party and other happy times. With all these advantages and drinks at cheaper prices it seems strange that membership should have declined.

Out in Hanley centre there was always plenty to see and do for the casual stroller, an itinerant speaker would often get up on his soap box, or the Salvation Army would set up a pulpit outside Sherwin's musical store adjacent to the market entrance. The Salvation Army citadel was in Glass Street, too, and after the service the band would lead the congregation back, the girls wearing black poke bonnets and shaking tambourines.

On winter evenings, White's roast tater machine would take its regular place outside the Westminster bank, selling bags of hot taters for threepence and affording customers the opportunity to warm their hands at the coal fired brazier, glowing red in the early dusk.

The same family conducted a business a few yards away in Market Street, now known as Huntbach Street, where they made and sold tasty ice cream. Just across the way were a fruit and veg. merchants who did a roaring trade around the streets of old Hanley with their produce on a horse and cart.

Another peculiar custom, during those long, hot, summer evenings of Double British Summer time, when the sky never completely darkened was the tradition of the 'Monkey Run', a courtship ritual dating from time immemorial. This exercise was equally enjoyed by both sexes and in Hanley the Monkey Run extended up and down Hope Street.

The custom was for all the youths, as young men were called before teenagers evolved, to walk down the street on one pavement, while the young girls promenaded on the other side. Greetings and friendly insults would be exchanged across the street, until couples paired off, perhaps to continue walking arm in arm or to disappear into the small cafe which stood half way down Hope Street. This was the house where the legendary Potteries author Arnold Bennet was born and had a plaque on the wall to this effect.

Few youngsters were interested in this, however, being more concerned with the first jukebox to appear in this area, which was to be found in this cafe. Other couples might make their way back up Hope Street, to cross the road into Lewis's arcade, there among the stalls could be found the latest in modern technology, an ice cream parlour, all chrome and shining levers, glass containers, whisks and spouts, which at the touch of a button would dispense a novelty, whipped ice cream. This was something different from the cones and wafers sold by the familiar 'Stop me and buy one' trike which stood outside Hanley Park during the summer. Here was a machine which could produce knickerbocker glories, banana splits, cherry sundaes and other delights. Served in tall, frosted glasses to eat with a long handled spoon, these new items were the height of sophistication, everyone envied the lucky lad who was invited to give his opinion of a new concoction.

Those youngsters who had a taste for something more substantial might well have turned to one of the nearby fish 'n' chip shops, many preferred Derricotts dining room up over the shop, which was situated in the High Street, adjacent to the market side entrance. The fish at Derricots were famed for being cooked in a crisp, rich, dark brown batter and the dining room would be packed at Saturday teatime, as shoppers called before completing their errands.

Hanley Wakes

Chapter Two

Up the Cockloft

Just opposite the chip shop was the large department store known to potters as 'Gipsy Balls', specializing in school and working clothing, with other drapery and soft goods.

Children were fascinated by the method in which the adults paid for their purchases, handing the money to the counter assistants, who would then reach up and pull an handle suspended from an overhead wire. Rattling down from a cage high in one corner of the store would come hurtling a container, to be unscrewed by the assistant, money for the goods placed inside and shot back up to the cashier perched in the little cage, who would make change, before sending the container on its return journey.

Lewis's store, the largest and most modern in Hanley during the immediate post war years, operated a similar system, but in this store the cashiers office was invisible. When goods were purchased

Photo loaned by Lewis's Ice Cream manufacturers

Hanley Market Square as a car park, complete with an attendants hut.

in Lewis's an article resembling a mortar shell would shoot down a pneumatic tube, the shop assistant would open it with a deft twist, replacing it in the tube whence it would disappear with a whoosh of compressed air, returning into a wire basket with change.

Woolworth's, the threepenny and sixpenny store as the legend over the door stated in those days, worked in a different manner. There, the girls (for all counter workers were girls then), stood inside rectangular stalls, with the goods laid out on counters before them for the customers to select and hand to the assistant. Years later, when the self service method was introduced, this caused considerable confusion as customers made to leave before completing payment.

Two of the many stores which have closed down or disappeared since the mid-forties Bratt and Dykes and Huntbach's, were both long established in Hanley. The building which housed Bratt and Dykes still stands on a corner of Trinity Street, housing a betting shop, a K. F. C and Cartlidge's drapery shop, where some interesting relics of the old Bratt and Dyke's store are displayed. The Huntbach store that used to stand in the Market Square has been swept away, together with so much of the old Hanley town centre, but at least the name of Huntbach survives, Market Street having been renamed such.

Like so many stores, the shops of Hanley took great pride in the quality and variety of their window dressing, unfortunately there was little available for display in those days of austerity, many of the items in the shop windows were cardboard replicas of goods that were rationed, or for export only.

Shops which specialised in selling sweets and tobacco were particularly hard hit by the rationing system. The sweet ration was restricted to six ounces of sweets or chocolate per week, obtainable only by exchanging coupons known as 'Personal Points' from your ration book. These were designated as either 'D' or 'E' coupons, an 'E' covering four ounces of confectionery and the 'D' two. Children would take great care in choosing their sweet ration, a favourite purchase being a quarter pound of 'Old Betty Plant's' peardrops a local make which averaged twelve sweets to a quarter, allowing two to be slowly sucked each day, then on Sunday a two ounce bar of chocolate could be savoured a square at a time.

Every household necessity was rationed after the war, even bread and potatoes, which had been readily available, went on the ration in 1947. Bread could only be obtained for ration coupons called 'Bread Units' and came in long, unsliced loaves made with dark flour. We used to give the grocer a penny to cut ours up on the bacon slicer, he'd very little else to slice!

In addition to foodstuffs, clothing and furniture were rationed, clothing was supplied against clothing coupons, apart from wooden soled clogs, such as those worn by Lancashire millworkers. Even as recently as the nineteen forties a cobblers shop in Hanley High Street still produced hand made clogs to measure and some potters found them ideal for work in the kilns or the sliphouse. Furniture was allocated on a priority system, according to the circumstances of the applicant and was made in the Utility pattern, mass produced and strictly functional, with no polish, veneers or frills. Solid no-nonsense stuff, ideal for a first home, but as implied by the name, strictly utilitarian.

The food rations were far from generous, calculated by the Ministry of Food to provide the necessary calories to maintain normal health and strength, they were supplemented by meals from the British Restaurant, that used to be in Cheapside. Miners, steel workers and other essential workers received extra rations, including more soap for the miners, who had to wash away the coal dust at home, there were no pit-head baths then.

Particular attention was always paid to the needs of the children, their health was carefully monitored by the school doctor and sun ray treatment prescribed to provide extra vitamins. The children at our school appreciated the food parcels which arrived from the U.S.A., containing luxuries like Maxwell House coffee, rich tinned fruit cake and tinned fruit.

We were rather less grateful for the vitamin supplements provided by our anxious parents. Such potions as cod liver oil and malt, which formed a thick glutinous mass on the spoon and was almost impossible to swallow, Haliborange, Parrishes Food and others came our way and each Saturday morning we were compelled to drink a hot mug of Senna tea.

Senna tea was a vile tasting, powerful laxative, obtained by steeping the pods of the Senna plant in hot water and leaving them to stew overnight. The dreaded brew would be standing on the black leaded kitchen grate when we children came downstairs on Saturday morning and a gallop down the yard to the outside toilet quickly followed. It may be that if we had been able to eat more fresh fruit, we would have been spared this ordeal, but although home grown fresh fruit was plentiful in season, tropical fruit such as oranges and bananas were in extremely short supply and strictly rationed.

I recall one little girl being offered a banana for the first time by a sailor home on leave who had bought a huge hand of the fruit back for the children, she promptly burst into tears at the sight! Oranges were even more difficult to obtain, often they were only made available to infant children who had blue ration books, sometimes to infants and schoolchildren who had green ration books and on rare occasions such as Christmas, to the whole family, including the buff ration books of the adults. When this happened, the shopkeeper had to cancel a panel on the back of the ration book in heavy indelible pencil, to ensure no-one got more than their fair share.

Home grown British fruit was available in season, such fruit as apples and pears were plentiful so were stone fruits, like plums Victoria and golden, cherries and damsons, although Nan had an old damson tree in her back garden, so we were weary of that particular fruit, stewed, in tarts or as jam. Dried fruit, including dried apple rings, apricots and prunes were all readily available, though we soon tired of either prunes or rhubarb with custard as a sweet.

By diligent searching, spending hours in long queues, it was sometimes possible to obtain limited quantities of unrationed goods to vary the family meals. Each household was required to register with certain shopkeepers and to deposit the ration books at that shop, in order to obtain the specified amount of rations each week.

This arrangement applied for groceries, we bought ours from Swettenhams who had a branch near my school, enabling me to collect the order on my way home. To the butcher, who was a friendly gent and kept a shop in Church Street, now Hillchurch Street and with a milk lady who came round with the milk ration in a pony and trap, sometimes leaving a welcome deposit of manure for the rhubarb patch in our back garden.

One of my regular jobs each Saturday morning, after I had completed a newspaper delivery round which took me from the top of Market Street to the other end of St. John Street, via the Rose Street area of Northwood, was to visit the town centre with instructions to join any queue I saw. Taking half a crown and a shopping basket, my first call would be at the old meat market, now known as The Tontines where it was generally possible to find broken biscuits off ration. More often than not, these would be my favourite Osbornes.

Photo donated

Shopping for the rations at the old meat market, notice the corner stone worn by the sharpening of knives.

Sometimes one of the butchers stall could find a lump of suet, which after steaming in a muslin bag, produced a filling, nourishing roll that was smeared with jam, treacle, or golden syrup. Alternatively, the cooked suet would be spread with minced meat and prepared like a Swiss roll, to be served with gravy and two veg; probably including onions from Dad's 'Dig for Victory' patch.

There were a certain amount of other goods available to supplement our food rations. One of the most popular and readily obtainable was the humble rabbit, which was a commonplace in the days before myxomatosis struck the bunny population.

At sixpence a pound, those rabbits formed the basis of many a tasty stew, thickened with pearl barley and slowly cooked in the blackleaded oven beside a coal fire. Many people compared the well cooked flesh of a rabbit with chicken and rabbit also made a nourishing pie, another dish which made full use of the vegetables from the school allotment. Our mothers were accustomed to spinning out the rations, a sixpenny ham hock, when boiled and carved would provide a plateful of ham sandwiches and with the addition of a packet of split peas to the ham bone, the family would enjoy a pot of soup.

Photo donated

The school dinner centre was opposite Glass Street School, so pupils were handy for their meals

The local pie shop did a roaring trade, selling meat and tater pies, steak pies and sausage rolls, with thick meat gravy at a penny a pint. All these goodies stayed piping hot in a steam oven and were good fillers for us at playtime or as we made our way to the dinner centre in Glass Street, opposite the school, which is now a carpark

At the dinner centre, we'd line up for our meal ticket, then again at the counters where the dinner ladies served us with portions of toad in the hole, sausage and mash or minced meat and tater pie, an equally big helping of a pud; like spotted dick or jam roly poly completed the feast!

We were growing children and had hearty appetites, so we'd run from our school in Turner Street along the High Street, to reach the front of the dinner queue and go round again for seconds. On our way back to school, many of us would call at the grocers for a penn'th of apples, two or three big sour Bramleys or Cox's went down well.

There used to be a fruit shop opposite the G.P.O. in Hanley which sold a large brown bag of ripe fruit for threepence, a popular stop if we were going to the pictures at the Palace.

If we went to the Saturday morning matinee at the Roxy, the threepenny rush as it was known, there was a bakery a little further up Church Street which baked hot buns especially for when the cinema emptied. Sticky buns containing a few currants were a penny each, plain ones two a penny and on Monday morning tu'pence bought a bag of five or six. There was liquorice root to be had from the herbalist, woody yellow stems to chew for flavour, locust which was an hard brown bean pod, that broke open to reveal sweet pink seeds and kali, a sweet sticky yellow powder in which to dip a moistened finger.

A disappointment was soya links, sold in tins described as pork or beef. When both ends of the can were opened a ring of seven sausages slid into the frying pan and smelled delicious. Unfortunately, they consisted entirely of soya packed in meat fat and had no flavour of their own.

Offal, such as liver was another meat product that was sometimes available without food coupons, so liver and onions often featured on the post war menu.

These scrounging expeditions sometimes produced strange results. There was the time when I met a schoolmate standing outside a shop in Broom Street, who told me they were selling oranges off the ration, in unlimited quantities. I rushed home to tell my parents, a neighbour overheard and gave me a penny for bringing her some. Returning to the shop, people were waiting halfway along St. John Street, but there were still some oranges remaining when I reached the counter. My five shillings bought two carrier bags full of fruit, a real novelty then, unfortunately, the shopkeeper had neglected to say that the fruit was of the bitter Seville variety intended to make marmalade! As the sugar ration was about a pound a week we had none to spare for this, we often used Savory & Moores saccharin tablets to sweeten our tea.

Another disaster befell when visiting a friend living in Bucknall Road. The row of terraced houses where he lived was built high above the roadway, on the opposite side of the road, below the flight of steep steps, with a handrail which led up to Windmill Street. There was a row of small shops, including a bike shop, a newsagents, a fish and chip shop and a little corner sweet shop. A patient queue had formed outside one shop and mindful of my standing orders I took my place in line. Some time later, I paid a shilling (5p) for two small cardboard boxes, which the shopkeeper told me to carry carefully. When I arrived home, my parents were none to pleased to find I'd bought two sixty watt bulbs, as our house was gas lit! This particular episode had an happy ending as a neighbour was glad to buy the unwanted bulbs.

Each individual block of terraced houses in Hanley formed a tight little self contained group and our block, lying a couple of streets away from the town centre was typical. Within a few paces of each other stood a pub, the Electric Bar as the locals called it, a newsagents, a drapers, the Yorkshire chip shop and a little way down Church Street another chip shop, the double of that which stands in Hanley museum today.

Our spiritual welfare was well catered for by two Welsh chapels, one at the corner of Mayer Street, the other in St. John Street. In addition, three houses had been converted into local shops by the simple economical process of fitting a counter in the front room and displaying goods in the house window.

One of these little shops, which used to stand in Church Street, where the car park is now, was unique to my knowledge in the range and variety of goods which were stocked.

The room was dominated by a large metal drum containing paraffin, hand pumped into a jug and sold at threepence a pint. This was essential fuel for the little nightlights which illuminated many bedrooms and outhouses, also being used to help light coal

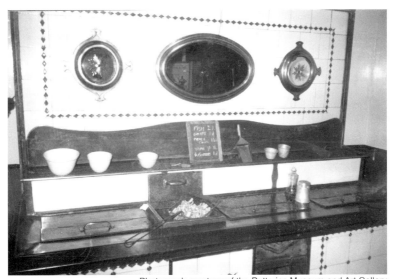

Photograph courtesy of the Potteries Museum and Art Gallery

Frying Tonight. "A sixpenny fish and threepenn'orth of chips, open please"

fires. Firelighters formed part of the stock in trade, consisting of four sticks of wood, bound with wire around a bundle of wood shavings. Other inflammable items included tapers, sticks and wooden spills. There were candles, wax nightlights to burn in a saucer, matches both household and safety. Bengal matches were on sale too, wrapped in a twist of waxed paper, for the shop also sold Bengal Lights, packets of sparklers and other fireworks. Each autumn for a few days before Bonfire Night the shop window would be dedicated to a display of fireworks, Guy Fawkes papier mache masks and a small centrepiece Guy.

Rolls of paper caps, ammunition for small boys cap pistols, were another popular item, like sweets called aniseed balls and gobstoppers, two for a penny, which lasted for ages and eked out the sweet ration. Incidentally, it was in this shop that I last spent a farthing, the smallest coin in the £. s. d. range, combining two with an ha'penny to buy a penny packet of spearmint. A row of glass jars on a convenient shelf contained loose, unwrapped boiled sweets from the local makers Old Betty Plants, which were the preferred choice of children as unwrapped sweets meant more toffee for your money.

Placards advertised the popular cigarettes of the day, Wild Woodbines, Passing Clouds and Park Drive. Unfortunately, these were another item that was unobtainable in those days, the only cigarette that love or money could buy was a Turkish brand called Pasha.

Beside the notebooks, the pencils and erasers on another shelf was a row of patent medicines, including Mothers' Friend and Indian Brandee, designed to soothe babies when their dummies were dipped into the mixture. Then there was that well known remedy Beechams Pills, second cousin to the dreaded senna tea, side by side with Carters' Little Liver Pills, Fenning's Fever cure and Woodwards' Gripe Water. Also present was a strange mixture called raspberry vinegar and olive oil, I never knew what that did!

Ample stocks of gas mantles, the main lighting source in many homes were cheek by jowl with rolls of gooey fly paper, to hang from the gaslight fixture and contain their full quota of insects when summer came. Colourful crepe paper to make Christmas decorations, there wasn't much that little shop didn't sell - but for some things you had to go into town.

A visit to Hanley at that time was incomplete without walking around the long established market, situated on the site of the present Potteries Shopping Centre, (see photo on next page) adjacent to the now sadly neglected St. John's church. Entering through the huge iron gates from Market Square, after threading through the parked vehicles, where the British Legion attendant sat in a little wooden kiosk, the shopper was plunged into a bustling scene.

Crowded aisles, thronged with eager shoppers, selecting fresh fruit and vegetables from the stalls, trying a pair of shoes, buying oatcakes or perhaps quenching their thirst with a drink from the trader who dispensed root beer, dandelion and burdock or sasparilla from huge, ornamental stoneware barrels.

If a nice cup of tea was the choice, there were several comfortable little cafes at the rear of the market, where the shopper could relax and survey the passing scene. Pottery stalls were prominent, as might be expected in the Potteries and the ware on show would be critically examined by the potters who had probably made it.

Photo loaned by Lewis's Ice Cream manufacturers

The car park attendants hut, seen here, went on to a bonfire on
V.E. day - the British Legion attendant escaped!

The Mecca for those of us who were schoolchildren then was at
the rear of the Market and spanned the length of the building.
Reached by steep stone steps, it was known as the Cockloft and
perched high above the throng, provided the ideal viewpoint to watch
for schoolmates, While you were waiting, the Cockloft offered plenty
of distractions, as it housed exotic creatures from the four corners
of the earth, in cages, bowls and glass cases. My favourite was a
sulphur crested cockatoo, on a perch at the top of the entrance
steps, children used to delight in teasing this bird, which must have
belonged to a sailor as it had a fine selection of swear words in its
vocabulary.

Other attractions displayed in the Cockloft included songbirds
such as linnets, canaries and budgies, lovebirds and parakeets, offered in a variety of containers, ranging from simple boxes covered
with mesh to large, expensive cages, finished in brass or chrome
and fitted with little ladders, mirrors and other playthings. Cats,
dogs and rabbits were on sale, with snakes, goldfish to feed with a
pinch of ants eggs, and day old chicks were also available. Black
ones and yellow ones, cheeping and climbing over each other. These
cost a penny each and we'd keep half a dozen warm in an old wicker

basket on the hearth until they were big enough to live in the backyard, free range birds before the expression was coined, to provide a few new laid eggs and the odd chicken to help out the meat ration.

Chapter Three

The slobs way to Botany Bay

When we'd had our fill of the Cockloft we left the market and walked down the 'Slobs', a path between St. John's church and Port Vale F. C football ground, which was constructed from old gravestones laid flat. (Photograph on following page). With a high corrugated iron fence on one hand, the boundary of the football club and the graveyard on the other side, the 'Slobs' had an eerie atmosphere in the dusk, being illuminated by a single flickering gas-lamp. We climbed the bank to the railway sidings serving the Hanley Deep pit, a favourite playground where the surface coal-mine workings known as the 'Hollies' extended for miles.

The name derived from the 1926 general strike, when striking workers mined the Holly Lane coal seam which outcropped here. We didn't know that at the time, but enjoyed playing in the area, where a scrapyard lay at the base of the hill we'd just climbed. The rusting remains of an old WW1 tank lay in this scrapyard and one day the axles of a broken rail truck were rolled down the hill, striking the tank and causing it to ring like a bell, a sound which carried all over Hanley. Grass, trees and shrubbery cover the industrial landscape now, but when we played on the Hollies, long before they became Hanley Forest park, the area was dominated by the pithead gear, the tall chimney, cooling tower and waste tip of Hanley Deep pit. The waste tip was known as the 'Aerial', having been made by an endless overhead cable carrying debris from the underground workings to the top of the hill.

Clinkers as large as houses stood beside the rough footpath, and a mound of steaming slurry contaminated with water draining from the mine, formed a deep pool at the base of the Aerial tip.

One afternoon during the bitter winter of 1947, a group of small boys dragged a sheet of corrugated metal from an Anderson

Memorial inscriptions can still be seen on these old grave stones which formed the 'slobs' footpath.

air-raid shelter up the snow covered slopes of the Aerial. The shelter tin', as children called it, was ideal for use as a sledge, being curved at the end allowing several sections to be bolted together and form a shelter which stood in every back garden. As the makeshift sledge descended the tip it was dragged higher up each time, until one daring lad took it almost to the top. Skimming down the hill, it bounced off a rock, crashing through the ice into the pool.

Luckily some adults picking coal from the waste saw the accident and crawling over the ice with the aid of ladders from the mine, pulled the boy from the freezing water. After he'd dried out in the colliery boiler room, he was able to return home safely, although his shrunken jersey and boots stiffened to shapeless lumps were minor tragedies in the days of clothes rationing.

Apart from the Hollies, another favourite playground lay in the fields of Botany Bay, not the one in Australia, but the grassy meadows, between the river Trent and the canal, near the 'Destructor' as the council run incinerator off Cromer Road was called. Those fields were alive with grass snakes, shy, harmless creatures which soon slithered away if they were disturbed. Such long thick grass, as high as a small boys waist, provided good grazing for cattle and horses, which meant that when I completed my paper round, early on an Autumn morning, it was easy to fill my cap with fresh mushrooms, delicious fried for breakfast.

Blackberries grew in the hedges surrounding those fields, one of our neighbours had a sour apple tree, so our family could be assured of a nice blackberry and apple tart.

In the springtime it was common to discover a birds nest in the hedgerow, collecting their eggs was a popular hobby then. Hanley museum in Pall Mall had cabinets full of them, all neatly blown through pinholes at each end and labelled. Every boy could identify the nest of a wren, a neat ball of tightly woven grasses, lined with soft moss or wool. Robins often nested in the strangest places, an old tin can might contain a clutch of their pink eggs. Lapwings, or peewits as they were called, made their nests in little hollows on the ground and laid the green and brown mottled eggs on the bare soil. The hen would sit on the eggs until someone almost trod on her, then fly off, dragging one wing low to decoy intruders away from the nest. We were always careful to take only one egg and avoid disturbing the nest, so the adult birds would return.

During one long summer holiday, a group of us armed ourselves with whatever tools we could obtain and made our way along

the sandy banks of the river Trent to a spot where the water ran deep and clear. Cutting at the base of the sand until heaps dropped into the water, we piled it up to dam the water flow. The banks became undermined, so that when our dam was broken we had a deep swimming hole, a perfect free alternative to Hanley baths.

In the meadows that lay between the canal and the Trent, there were many other opportunities for mischief. We tied ropes to the trees on the Birches Head side of the Trent and Mersey canal, then

Years later the water's still inviting. Ropes still hang on the trees, boys still swing and drop in.

emulated Johnny Weismuller in his role as Tarzan by swinging across to the opposite bank, while emitting a loud jungle yell.

Sometimes this would become a genuine scream, as mum's clothesline, cunningly disguised as the jungle vine, snapped and deposited the 'Lord of the Jungle' into the semi-stagnant canal water. Swimming in the canal was not recommended, rumour was that leeches lived in the murky depths. We knew that unwanted pets were sometimes drowned there, by anyone unwilling to pay sixpence for them to be humanely killed at the old police station, behind Hanley Town Hall. Certainly rodents lived around the canal at that time, we used to see them while we played at pirates on the derelict hulk of an old canal barge, lying semi-submerged among the bulrushes at the canal side.

When we tired of pretending that the passing barges, carrying china clay from the West country to the potbanks, or loads of ware to the distributors were treasure galleons, we would ambush the vermin. Some of us would throw pebbles at the rodents, others were armed with Daisy or Gat air rifles or pistols firing a small. 177 calibre pellet. Others had bows, made from garden canes, using arrows flighted with pieces of card and tipped with anything from small nails to the points from empty ballpoints. The ultimate deterrent was a powerful aluminium catapult, designed for use by anglers, to throw ground bait.

This magnificent weapon had a thumb grip socket and was fitted with double lengths of quarter inch rubber, attached to a calf leather sling. Using a cylindrical ball bearing as ammunition, this catapult was capable of killing a rodent on the opposite bank of the canal.

Plentiful supplies of ball bearings, together with ball races could be obtained from the garage at the top of Lime Kiln bank, which was busy breaking down war surplus vehicles for scrap and spares. 15 cwt;  Bedford lorries, jeeps and trailers, Bren gun carriers and D.U.K.W's, (pictured above) which were amphibious vehicles designed in 1942 having four wheel drive and could proceed at well over 30 m.p.h. on land . D.U.K.W.'s were equally at home in the water, being capable of a speed averaging five knots, carrying a two and a half tons payload and requiring a two man crew.

For several years following the war, these versatile vehicles were used as patrol craft at seaside resorts, some are still in use today as sightseeing tour attractions on the river Thames.

Right:
Ferret Scout Car,
maximum speed 45
m.p.h., climbed a
slope of 1 in 2,
weighed 5 tons and
had a crew of two.
It was used with ar-
moured formations
for reconnaissance.
Its main gun was a
0.30 in. Browning.
Below:
Saracen Armoured

Personnel Carrier for 12 men.
Maximum speed 35 m.p.h. Hull
and turret made of welded armour plate. Total weight some
11 tons. 0.30 in. machine gun.
Below: Chieftain main battle
tank. 53 tons of mobile fire
power. Armament : 120mm
high-velocity gun.

The Stalwart dual purpose vehicle was designed as a replacement, having about twice the cargo capacity of the D.U.K.W., a considerable speed advantage on both land and water, and also required a crew of two.

Nearest equivalent to the Bren carrier was the armoured personel carrier (A.P.C.). The Bren carrier was designed to provide light armour protection to the two man crew operating a Bren machine gun and was an open topped tracked vehicle. Its successor, the A.P.C. was much heavier and was designnhed to carry infantry under cover.

The Jeep was eventually superseded by the familiar, versatile Land Rover which had a competitor in the four wheel drive Austin Champ. For armoured reconnaissance the Ferret scout car entered service, armed with a .30 calibre gun turret mounted with and with a top speed ofmore than 40m.p.h. A variant of the Ferret was equipped with four anti-tank missiles, two fitted beside the turret and two stored internally.

We left the garage at the top of Lime Kiln bank with a sack of ballbearings, for use in our catapult and some carefully selected ballraces, there was a special use for these latter items as an essential component of one of our favourite home made toys.

Proceeding back to town through Northwood Park, pausing for a drink from the fountain, which used to be surmounted by a statue, that stands in Fountain Square today, we stood watching workers filling in the slit trenches which had been dug as protection against war time air raids.

Our next errand was a call at Palmers' huge timber yard, occupying a large site in central Hanley, between Charles Street and Gilman Street, presently occupied by a shopping precinct and offices. We begged some wooden laths from one of the men working in the yard, who was well known to us for supplying wood shavings and sawdust as bedding for our pets, which in my case included two large chinchilla rabbits who lived in the coalhouse.

After extracting a promise from our friend that he would save us some scrap wood for Bonfire Night and that we could call and collect it each week, we called into Gilberts' chip shop, next to the timber yard, before going home with our loot.

Next morning we began constructing our new toys. Taking some old floorboards, salvaged from a demolition site we assembled a sturdy frame, about six feet long by two wide, using rusty three in; nails, stored in a national Dried Milk tin. One of the laths we'd obtained from Palmers' was securely nailed to the rear of the platform, then with the assistance of a red hot poker a hole was burned through the other strut which was fixed to the front and fastened with a well greased nut and bolt to swivel freely

Having shaped the ends of the struts with an old spokeshave, the circular ballraces were tapped tightly onto each end, then using a red hot nail held in pliers, holes were made for securing screws. The ballraces wore through in time and had to be replaced with old pram wheels. With the addition of a short piece of wood screwed by one of the rear wheels for use as a footbrake, we had a 1947 model ball racing cart. Resorting once more to a red hot nail, the name 'Silver Bullet' was burned onto the cart, after the latest firework of the day. Our cart received a coat of khaki paint, available by the bucketful and when it was dry we pulled it to the top of Eaton Street for a trial run.

The Author

Our New Cart Wheels - from the old pram

Fortunately, cars were few and far between then, many were still laid up on blocks where they had been for the duration of the war, because of petrol rationing. Lying prone on the cart, nose only a couple of inches from the ground and steering with both hands on the front axle, those carts gave a terrific sensation of speed, hurtling along on ballrace wheels. At the bottom of Eaton Street a right turn into Keelings Road carried the cart to Lime Kiln bank and the momentum after descending this would propel the cart into Leek Road or up to Werrington Road.

The carts served a useful purpose too, all through the Wakes holiday we would wait by the Station Road bus stop to meet holiday-makers on their way to Blackpool or Rhyl. They were pleased to load their suitcases onto our cart and have them taken to the station and we were glad to be rewarded with some coppers. We'd wait at Stoke Station for trains full of returning potters and offer the same transport service, the three weekends of Hanley Wakes were a golden opportunity to earn some pocket money. Nothing came easily then, if we wanted any money we had to earn it and our home made carts gave good service.

They transported coal bricks from the coal merchants yard in Grafton Street, which were a fuel made out of coal slack and dust, mixed with cement and compressed into six inch square blocks. Those coal bricks did a lot to help out the coal ration and with coke collected from Etruria gasworks in Garner Street, we walked miles with our little trucks delivering winter fuel around Hanley.

Anything we earned went to help out the family budget or to pay subscriptions for the Scouts, A.T.C or youth club. Clearing snow from the front steps and pathways for people was a good way to earn money in the winter. I had a paper round and delivering the papers on Christmas Eve to a house with a jolly party going I think I was probably one of the first paperboys to knock and wish my customers a 'Merry Christmas', to be presented with a shilling!

It was a different world in those days, anyone would give a child a copper or a sweet to run an errand and a child could safely knock on any door to ask for a drink or to use the toilet. Life wasn't all school and part-time jobs, though, we played games in the street and each game had its season. No sooner would one child appear with a top and whip chalking an intricate design on the top, than all the local children would be playing top and whip. Then overnight, tops and whips would disappear and the vogue would be alleys, or marbles, played along the gutters, a tragedy if your favourite 'glassie' disappeared down a drainage grid, or 'ringie', involving placing the marbles in a ring and taking turns with a 'shottie' to try and knock one out of order and win it.

Youngsters played with hoops too, although we called them 'bowlers', confusing in an age when most men wore hats. Our hoops weren't the genteel light cane ones, either, but heavy iron ones, obtained from the potbank at the top of Festing Street, their original purpose was to secure the staves in the wooden barrels in which ware was packed for delivery. The girls would join in playing hoops and in French cricket using an old tennis ball. Players defended their legs with the bat in this game and the object was to score as many runs as possible before being struck on the leg.

There was another game played with a ball, known as Queenie-io-coco, where one player threw a ball over a shoulder to be caught by the others to the call of 'Queenie-io-coco', the thrower would turn and try to guess who had the ball, if correctly guessed they'd change places. We played hopscotch, with a pitch chalked on the tarmac and a local variant, which had a circular pitch, rather like a Catherine wheel, with 'home' in the middle.

Generally speaking the girls were content with their own pastimes, for reasons best known to them, they derived endless pleasure out of tucking their dresses into their knickers and standing on their hands against a wall. When they tired of this they'd take someone's baby for a walk in its pram, or get out their French knitting, consisting of a wooden cotton spool, having four small tacks knocked into the top. Using scraps of brightly coloured wool, which would be twisted around the tacks and lifted, rather like crocheting, an endless multi coloured plait would emerge from the base of the spool. This hobby had a practical use, the yards of plait could be sewn together to form a cot blanket or small rug.

Girls had another way to earn some pocket money, they would weave bracelets out of electrical wire, which was insulated in many different colours, several strands woven together produced a wrist bracelet. Such was the scarcity of consumer goods then, that these bracelets became fashionable, even some of the chainstores in Hanley sold them.

Meanwhile, we'd be occupied playing cricket, with the stumps chalked on a wall and the width of the street deciding the length of the pitch, emulating our heroes, the famous Don Bradman and the Compton twins.

We might play Rally and go next, this was a game rather like hide and seek, in which one player was 'on' while the others ran to hide in entries (the alleyways which gave access to the back doors of our homes), in the brick air raid shelters which still stood in the streets, or behind the static water tanks, constructed for use in the event of a firebomb raid,

Whatever game was being played was always liable to be interrupted by someone deciding not to play anymore, or being called in for a meal. When this happened, the cry went up, "All in, the games broke up, so and so has broke it up".

Our parents ensured we had a family outing during the Wakes, as well as a visit to the fair. Depending on finances, this might take the form of a ride on a bus belonging to the Brown company, which was appropriately painted khaki. This fleet of single deck 'buses had seats composed of wooden slats, resembling park benches and the terminus was near the Palace cinema. In common with all buses during the late 1940's a conductor would collect the fares, wearing an harness which carried rows of coloured tickets, complete with a little punch for cancelling return tickets.

The conductor would ring a bell to signal the driver to start the bus and call out the name of each stop, quite often on these local outings our destination would be the village of Bagnall.

Returning from these outings we'd get off the bus in Bucknall Road, where there stood a row of small shops including one on the corner which stocked a huge range of tinware. Such items as waterbottles and snapping tins, for colliers to carry their food and drink down into the mine, pots and pans, kettles and 'Drawplates'- large metal sheets with a handle, designed to be placed before household coal fires and increase the draught up the chimney, so 'drawing' the fire, which burned more brightly. There were dustbins and tin baths, the type which hung from a nail in many back kitchens.

Among other useful gadgets this shop stocked an item called a 'Tinkers Friend' consisting of two flexible pieces of thin metal, separated by an asbestos washer on a self tapping screw. This was used to repair small holes in pots and pans, so the item could be re-used.

Also sold here were D-I-Y chimney cleaners, a small packet of chemicals forming a two inch cube, designed to be placed on a brightly burning fire, causing a chemical reaction to clear soot from the chimney - at least that's what the packet claimed!

A little further along stood a Chinese laundry, where dad would sometimes have his best white shirt washed and starched for special occasions. Normally, he wore a loose collar, secured by front and back collar studs, we learned some novel phrases when dad struggled with his back stud. Then there was an oatcake shop, with a large sack of oatmeal and a scoop just inside the door, Each oatcake shop had their own recipe and I'd visit this shop each Sunday morning for half a dozen warm ones, for the traditional potters' Sunday breakfast of cheese and bacon with lots of 'dip' for the oatcakes fat from the bacon, full of cholesterol, something else we'd never heard of!

Dad had a favourite Potteries dialect saying if I was slow on these errands, "Thay losukst in that cheer as tho' thayt sennatucked", which translated as "You sit in that chair as if you were constipated".

Our favourite among these shops and the reason for leaving the bus here was the shop of the 'Penny Pop' man. This gent was the proud owner of an Heath Robinson gadget, all glass containers, copper pipes, valves and glass cylinders with which he prepared the famous brew. After taking our order for the flavour of our choice, he would select the appropriate phial from a rack of brightly coloured liquids, labelled 'Sasparilla', 'Ginger Beer' etc; after much twisting of wheels, opening and closing of valves, hisses and splutters of gas a tablet was dropped into a jar, he'd turn a tap and the desired beverage would be decanted, to be poured into a bottle which was secured with a stopper, a rubber band and an arrangement of twisted wires. Those bottles of 'Penny Pop' were great thirst quenchers on a hot day. With a good shake and by quickly releasing the stopper, they served as water pistols too.

Another character we would see in Hanley was the gent with an old plate camera on a tripod who used to ply his trade outside the 'French Horn'. Having suitably posed his client, avoiding buses turning the roundabout into Piccadilly he would duck beneath a black cloth and focus the camera. Dipping the resulting print into a can of fixer, the customer received a sepia toned picture.

Then there was the white bearded old gent who used to drive an open top bullnose Morris car. His motor was a golden oldie, even by the standards of the 1940's, when prewar vehicles were just returning to the roads after the war, although petrol was still rationed.

With a polished brass radiator, topped by a temperature gauge and fitted with running boards, a side mounted handbrake and the battery exposed on one running board, his car wouldn't have been out of place in the London to Brighton vintage car rally.

Prominently displayed on the windscreen was a notice, 'All lifts at your own risk' and small boys took this to be an invitation to ask for a lift, each time we saw him parked outside the 'Grapes' pub at the bottom of Market Street. All our requests were refused, until the Saturday when he offered three of us a ride to Northwood Park on his way home.

With four on board, the old car struggled to climb steep Market Street, it made better time down Eaton Street, nearly as fast as our home made carts. Still, it was thrilling to ride in any car , ownership of a vehicle was generally restricted to such as the local doctor then, no parking problems in those days.

A knife grinder was another character who regularly visited our part of Hanley, mounted on a rusty upright bike. He'd collect any cutlery, scissors or tools which needed sharpening, lift the back wheel of his bike onto a stand and fix a driving belt to a grindstone fitted between the handlebars. Pedalling madly away, the grindstone sprayed a shower of sparks as implements were sharpened, nearly as good as a Catherine Wheel we thought. It was a disappointment when the knifegrinder arrived without his bike one day, so we followed him around the corner hoping to watch the free fireworks. There he was, busily sharpening knives on a sandstone door step, a traditional method then, as can be seen by the grooves in the stonework of the 'Tontines', a reminder of when this was the meat market and butchers sharpened their knives here.

The rag and bone man frequented the streets of Hanley, too, with his cry "Old iron, rag bone". An old garment, useless even for a rag rug, the bedspring which supported a featherbed, he'd take almost everything and reward the donor with a balloon, or a windmill on a stick.

Hanley Wakes

A blast of a bugle and a shout of 'Hokey Pokey', heralded the arrival of the ice cream man. He had an unusual vehicle, a little two wheeled cart, holding a container of ice cream, packed about with dry ice, steaming in the sun. His little cart, with a brightly coloured canopy, was drawn by a sad little donkey and his arrival attracted a crowd of children, holding basins for threepence worth of ice cream and free wafers.

Once a week a man came round selling salt blocks and crying his wares, it seemed that his call always foretold a shower, for we had our own ways of forecasting the weather. For example, if the engine whistles from the shunting yards at Hanley could be heard clearly, rain was on the way and mum would remark "It's gone black over Bill's mothers".

Hopefully, we'd travel further afield, maybe we'd ride in a 'Creamline' taxi to Hanley station by the Grand Hotel and catch a steam train to a local beauty spot. Of course, we'd travel third class, in those little carriages, which had no corridors and consequently, no toilets. It didn't pay to drink too much before an outing!

We might travel to Trentham Gardens as Trentham had its own station then and hundreds of daytrippers visited the Gardens. Here, we could ride in the launches on the lake, walk through the pine woods to the swimming pool or maybe ride the miniature railway there and back.

Alternatively, we could board the train at Bucknall station, the platforms still stand by the Kwik Save stores and journey to Alton Towers. It was a long climb up to the Towers, which at that time were far from today's theme park. Flowers and shrubs were the main attractions then, although there was a huge model railway which fascinated small boys and dads.

Chapter Four

The daily round

In common with many other terraced houses in Stoke on Trent immediately following the last war, our Hanley home lacked a bathroom and consequently we were regular patrons of Hanley baths, which used to be at the top of Lichfield Street adjacent to the Town Hall, immediately opposite St. Johns' school. The slipper or private baths featured a large white cast iron bath enclosed in a cubicle, the price of admission was threepence for which you received the loan of a large Turkish towel and a piece of carbolic soap. The water supply was controlled from outside the cubicle by an attendant clad in a boiler suit and wellingtons, who used a special key to open the mixer valves. Shower baths and Turkish baths, together with a steam room were also available. Privacy was at a premium in the showers which stood in a corridor where they were only separated by curtains.

Swimming baths were housed in the same building, with steps leading into the water, which had an all pervading smell of chlorine. A gutter running around the pool at water level provided a convenient handhold for tired swimmers and iron bars in the ceiling spanned the baths, from one spectators gallery to the other. It was common for some child to fall into the water from these bars, deliberately or after losing their grip while crawling to the opposite balcony. Mixed bathing nights were a popular social occasion, with Saturdays normally the province of children and the baths were also well used by the Water Polo club and school classes. Organised and uniformed activities played a large part in the leisure time of the post war youth of Hanley, the boy Scouts in particular were extremely active in the area. St. John's Baptist schoolrooms, which were in Charles Street, the troop attached to St. Matthew's church and the Tinkers clough boys were all closely associated with the development of Kibblestone camp at that time, helping to plant thousands of daffodil bulbs and to build the bridge over Daffodil Dell.

Drum and bugle corps bands were an important part of the Boys Brigade then, their marching tunes used to sound out around our street every Sunday morning, competing with the music of the Church Lads.

Any boy who grew up during the Second World War could hardly fail to be interested in 'planes, the Empire News Sunday paper carried a league table on the front page listing the number of enemy aircraft destroyed each week and though Hanley escaped comparatively lightly, we prided ourselves on our ability to identify every type of aircraft in the sky.

Personally, I remember noticing that when planes began to fly high enough to leave a vapour trail, that this would quickly expand to cover a cloudless sky, often leading to rain. Many lads joined the Air Training Corps, in anticipation of a chance to fly in Service aircraft, learn the basics of a trade and, like myself, fire off live rounds on the .22 rifle range. I was interested in the trade of Armourer at the time and the classes must have left a deep impression on me as I still recall the specification and the procedure for stripping the .303 Browning machine gun, fitted to the Spitfire, should the M.O.D require them! We enjoyed visiting Meir aerodrome, which was still operating Slingsby basic gliders and using de Havilland Tiger Moth biplanes as towing aircraft, although it had

This is an early Hurricane Fighter, it was a black Mk IIc armed with four cannon, which intercepted bombers over Etruria.

probably been accepted by then that Meir was unlikely to become an airport for Stoke on Trent. Impromptu flying displays by passing R. A. F and Allied aircraft were a regular occurrence, I clearly remember standing on the Aerial dirt tip of Hanley Deep Pit, watching a squadron of Mk.XX Spitfires fly below me, being on a steam train to Trentham which was buzzed by a Chipmunk trainer and being on the roof of the Capitol cinema as a Hornet fighter flew past inverted with one engine feathered. Such low level flying was shortly to be banned, in the interests of public safety, but before that happened people all over the Potteries watched a Meteor jet fighter performing impressive aerobatics, finally disappearing from view in a steep dive. It transpired that the aircraft had crashed on Wolstanton Marsh, avoiding nearby property when an engine failed. My childhood home has long since disappeared under the red ash of a car park, only the back garden wall remains on one of the highest points in Hanley. When I was a boy, the back bedroom window afforded views across Cliffe Vale to the woods at Keele and I remember standing there one moonlight night during the war, as two enemy bombers flying parallel with the main railway line, fired at the gasometers on Etruria gas works. They were being pursued by a Hurricane nightfighter and later the fields at Berryhill were illuminated by the flames from dozens of incendiary bombs, jettisoned by the bombers.

A Spitfire fighter, designed by Reginal Mitchell and used by the Royal Air Force during the Battle of Britain.

Hanley Wakes

There was a different atmosphere to Sunday then, which set it apart from every other day. No shrieking factory hooter woke Hanley's potters that day, instead the bells of St. John's and other churches rang out. Sunday meant the traditional breakfast of bacon, cheese and oatcakes, there were probably even more oatcake producers then than now. Granted, most of them were cottage industries, making oatcakes in the front room. There's at least one of the old style oatcake shops which continues full production today, 'The Hole in the Wall', which has been situated in Waterloo Street, Hanley for decades although the latest equipment, including an industrial microwave oven has been installed.

'The Hole in the Wall' bakes the full range of popular Potteries delicacies, cooked in the time-honoured manner on a hotplate. Each oatcake bakery has its own recipe for the batter mix, containing stone ground flour and sea salt among the ingredients, the Potteries oatcake could be described as an health food, seen here being prepared by the proprietor, Glen. A measured portion of batter is

St. John's Church had a beautiful Peal of bells, clocks which were visible from most of central Hanley and unique stained glass windows.

58

poured carefully onto the hotplate, spread out to size by the young ladies in this picture (Photo 25) and as one side cooks flipped over with a palette knife, rather like a pancake in reverse! The freshly baked items are then cooled on a wiremesh rack, although there's a steady demand for a "Dozen warm ones", from customers peering through the shop window. Variations on the theme include both plain and fruited pikelets, crumpets and a popular line at 'The Hole in the Wall', oatcakes hot from the

The spotless tiled walls and worktops at the 'Hole in the Wall' where the traditional batter for oatcakes is being prepared

A queue forms by the window for oatcakes, crumpets or pikelets hot from the baxton.

stove, with the traditional filling of cheese and bacon, sausages and others to taste.

What used to be a cottage industry has now become an hygienic business, all gleaming stainless steel and spotless work surfaces, which continues to produce a favourite local delicacy.

After breakfast the children would go to Sunday school while dinner was prepared, despite rationing Sunday dinner was dedicated to roast beef and two veg; with lashings of gravy. In many homes the meat would be roasted in the cast iron, blackleaded oven beside an open coal fire, above the fire hung a smoke blackened kettle, suspended on a pothook, the oven shelves were solid cast iron, wrapped in pieces of old blanket on winter nights, making perfect bed warmers.

Dinner would often be washed down with a glass of Burtons' ginger beer and after the dishes had been washed using hot water drawn from the tank with its huge brass tap, that flanked the other side of the firegrate, the family prepared for a good walk. It was the custom to alternate visits to the grandparents with a walk in the fresh air. The outskirts of Hanley was quite rural in those days and a favourite walk was down Birches Head Lane to the canal towpath, returning home by way of the allotments at Northwood and through the park. All that exercise gave everyone an appetite for tea, consisting of bread and home made jam, the ubiquitous damson. A victoria sponge and bottled fruit, prepared the previous Autumn and stored on the cellar stillage.

When tea was finished we dressed in our Sunday best, ready for church - the clothes worn on Sunday were strictly for that day, we'd change into clean old clothes when we returned. Arriving at church and collecting hymn and prayer books from the sides man, the children ensured their attendance cards had been stamped with a star, a certain number had to be amassed to ensure a place on the Sunday school outing.

Today was a special day, it was the Sunday school anniversary and the children were all dressed in new clothing, especially bought for the day, in order to appear on the stage and sing before the congregation.

Earlier, the children had called on relatives and friends to display their finery and now it was time for them to show how well they'd learned their singing lessons. Such childish favourites as 'Jesus, friend of little children' and 'Jesus bids us shine' were sung,

Brownstone sinks like this one are now in demand as troughs for garden plants. The object by the sink is a dolly-peg, used in the dolly-tub.

ending with a solo of the 23rd; Psalm. After the service, the family shook hands with the minister and exchanged greetings with friends and neighbours, before making their way home down the quiet streets.

Sunday used to be a quiet day, the shops were closed, as on Thursday afternoons and even the wireless programmes were different. 'Two way family favourites', from servicemen and women stationed in Germany, Aden, Egypt, Cyprus and other postings, on the Light Programme, with the Palm Court orchestra and 'Sunday Half Hour' in the evening.

Monday was traditionally washday, before the advent of automatic washers and tumbledryers. Our house was no exception to the rule and mother would rise earlier than usual, working by candlelight in the winter, for the gaslight had never been connected in the back kitchen. This room had bare brick walls and the laths which supported the roof tiles were open to view.

A brownstone sink under the window was fed by a single cold water tap, with a lead pipe running down the wall and always liable to freeze in winter.

Using a white enamel bucket, mum filled the gas boiler and the coal fired copper in the opposite corner, then lit a fire under this. Her supplies of Oxydol washing powder, 'Speedy as a Spitfire', according to the adverts, of Reckitt's Blue, a strange powder contained in a small cloth bag, added to the washing to make whites whiter were to hand. Also present was a packet of Robin starch and a bar of Sunlight washing soap to scrub stubborn stains.

Photograph courtesy of the Potteries Museum and Art Gallery

The old tin bath hangs behind the mangle. On wash day and bath night the only source of hot water was the copper.

After sorting the washing into separate heaps of white and coloured articles the water in the gas boiler was ready to receive the first load of whites, to be tipped in, liberally sprinkled with Oxydol and left to boil. Meanwhile, the dolly tub and dolly peg were dragged to the copper, filled with warm water ready for the wash to be agitated by hand, before as much water as possible was extracted by the wooden rollers of the mangle. This massive implement stood on cast iron wheels and was operated by hand cranking a large iron wheel to turn the rollers. An iron thumbscrew on the top of the mangle controlled the pressure of the rollers and this was screwed down as tightly as possible to squeeze out water, making the handle more difficult to turn.

Should any of the children be at home on washday, as we were for the Wakes, they were pressganged into turning the handle.

It was a warm sunny day, with a stiff breeze, a "good drying wind", mum remarked as she pegged out the washing . Our washing line was very efficient, being attached by a pulley to the high pole which carried the wireless aerial from the top of the garden to the chimney and down to the wireless set.

Next day, two flat irons were placed on the rings of the gas cooker in readiness for the ironing. The crockery was removed from the kitchen table, which was covered with an old blanket and having drawn one of the kitchen curtains, to prevent the brilliant sunshine from extinguishing the coal fire, which heated the oven containing the lobby for our tea, the ironing commenced. A flat iron was selected and tested for the correct temperature by the approved method of spitting on the heated surface. If the moisture hissed and quickly evaporated, the iron was ready, any hotter would result in a iron shaped brown scorch mark on a garment. Ironing for a family of eight was a long job and in the evening we sat down to a bowl of the potters' stew, lobby, a mixture of meat and veg; thickened with pearl barley and cooked all day in the fireside oven. Despite the August heatwave our bowls were soon emptied.

"Time" has been called at the Observatory pub, now standing derelict on one of the steepest hills in Hanley

Ex-servicemen were still returning home after active service in the war and I accompanied dad on a visit to an old friend of his who had been with the 'Forgotten army', fighting in the Far East. The returning soldiers' home had been decorated with flags and bunting, together with a hand painted sign reading 'Welcome back, Bill' and dad invited his mate to join him for a drink in the Observatory pub, on the corner of Smith Street.

The celebration served a dual purpose as there had been a recent addition to our family, an excuse to wet the baby's head. Despite the sign on the pub door reading, 'Sorry no beer or fags', the adults were able to get merry, while I sat on the step with a bottle of pop.

When the landlord finally placed a towel over the pumps, dad invited his long lost friend to come and see the baby and they walked up the street singing 'Roll out the Barrel'.

Mother was still confined to home after baby's birth and was sitting in the parlour, where the infant lay in a makeshift cradle, one of the drawers from a chest of drawers.

Dad's friend was feeling unwell and leaned on the mantelpiece, which was surmounted by a huge overmantle with a multitude of mirrored shelves, holding my parents collection of Goss china souvenirs of their courtship. Also on the mantelpiece was grandad's mounted display of army cap badges, he'd been in the Garrison Artillery during the first war, together with two small calibre artillery shells, carefully polished each week with Brasso. As our visitor turned away from the fire, he knocked a shell on to the tiled hearth, where it exploded. Having stood on the shelf as an ornament for almost thirty years, the missile was only partially live, nevertheless it gouged holes in the plaster at ceiling height and smashed most of the ornaments . When the explosions ended, Gran dad was able to enter from the kitchen and after he'd ensured everyone was unhurt his language turned the air blue.

Grandad was a real character who'd served as a senior N. C. O and still wore a waxed moustache, he was a kindly man who took me to school on my first day at Broom Street infants and bribed me to stay with a quarter of dolly mixtures. A regular at the nearby Welsh chapel, he could always be found sitting in the Beehive pub after morning service, a pint of black and tan before him, taking the air by the open door and playing crib with his cronies. His Sunday dinner would be kept warm between two plates in the oven and then he'd lie on his bed until tea.

This routine continued for years until the Sunday we returned from a walk with a bunch of fragrant May blossom which was taken into the kitchen by one of the youngsters and handed to mum. We were amazed when she threw the flowers in to the bin, saying that it was a sign of a death in the family to bring May blossom into the house. Nothing would console her and later that day, when a wild bird flew in through the open back door and fluttered around the house, she was convinced something dreadful was imminent. When I went to call grandad for his tea that afternoon, I was unable to waken him, he had died in his sleep.

It was the custom in those post-war days for the deceased to be returned to their homes in an open coffin during the day before the funeral ceremony, to be viewed by friends and neighbours who wished to pay their last respects. Our typical two up, two down terraced house was cramped when the coffin was placed on trestles by the parlour window and a faint, but noticeable sickly sweet smell filled the air.

A side table covered with a snowy white cloth stood by the door, holding a plate of finger biscuits and glasses of sherry to offer the visitors, while wreaths and flowers were propped against the outside wall. The undertaker arrived and asked the family to wait in the kitchen, while the lid of the coffin was closed, then the Rolls-Royce hearse was loaded, the mourners boarded the Humber Super Snipe cars and the cortege left.

Every house in the street had the curtains drawn as a last mark of respect and as the sad procession proceeded slowly to Hanley cemetery, men on the pavement doffed their hats. After the internment the mourners returned to our house for the traditional funeral tea. A huge tea urn and trestle tables had been borrowed from the Salvation Army, friends had loaned an assortment of dining chairs, crockery and cutlery for this ceremonial meal.

There was seedy cake and a ham salad, beer and wine, for everyone then paid regular contributions to a life policy, in order to ensure a 'good send off'. The Ministry of Food made a special allowance of ration points for such occasions as weddings and funerals, one of my little siblings was so impressed by the Lyons chocolate rolls in gaily coloured wrappings, that he enquired when someone else would die so that we could have another party!

As I recall, it was at about this time that people first heard the expression 'Squatters' and were puzzled until it was explained that the term applied to someone who unlawfully occupied property. It appeared that several families who were particularly badly affected by the post war housing shortage had scaled the perimeter wall surrounding the Territorial Army barracks in Ivy House road and moved into the Nissen huts which were standing empty after the war. By all accounts the authorities had served notice on the squatters to quit the huts, this had been refused and rumour had it that the unauthorised occupants were to be evicted, forcefully if necessary. The crowd which gathered to watch were disappointed, it appears, as the eviction was carried out sympathetically. The squatters being re-housed on a temporary basis until permanent accommodation was available.

Shortly afterwards, the first 'prefabs' appeared in Hanley, consisting of sectional panels which were assembled on concrete bases to form sturdy bungalows. These pre-fabricated homes had central heating, an indoor bathroom and a refrigerator. With wall insulation and with electricity and plumbing built in, they were desirable properties, intended as temporary homes, which survived longer than expected

Whole areas were covered by the prefabs, around Warner Street, off Broad Street and on vacant ground around Broom Street, a favourite playground for my schoolmates.

Chapter Five

Autumn 1947 - Winter draws on

At the final Scout camp for that Autumn, our patrol enjoyed sitting around a blazing campfire, singing and telling stories. As the fire burned down and darkness closed in it was the custom to tell each other ghost stories and two of the Scoutmasters had tales to recount about their school-days in Hanley. One concerned a school where all the young men among the teachers were called into the forces when the war began. It seems the bigger boys, including our friend were asked to help with some of the caretakers duties and among these fixing the blackouts and turning out the gas lights after school.

The boys needed to climb a stepladder to reach the chains controlling the lights and the speaker said, while they were doing this, all saw a boy leave one of the classrooms, cross the hall and go into the cloakroom.

Their task completed, it remained for them to lock the doors and hand the keys into the lodge on the way home, when they realised their schoolmate was still in the cloakroom.

When they looked in the room they were amazed to find it empty, there were two doors, that opened onto the hall and the door to a steep flight of steps, which was locked!

Our friend went on to say that the cloakroom only contained some washbasins and a row of coat racks, there was nowhere for anyone to hide and he often wondered what he saw in the school hall that night, We sat quietly around the embers of the camp fire, listening to the noises of the night while another older Scout told us a story about his school-days. He'd been a pupil at a school in Northwood and a nearby house had the reputation of being haunted. It seems that groups of children would assemble in the dusk, listening to eerie screams and watching strange lights in the deserted front room.

These disturbances reached such a peak said the narrator, that the police eventually investigated and after a search a body was discovered buried under the quarry tiles in the parlour. Apparently, the body was that of a young man who had been missing for some years and the case was documented in the local paper at the time.

It's over fifty years since I heard these stories and the story tellers have long since passed on, but I know none of us youngsters slept well that night.

Autumn arrived suddenly that year, as household fires added to the perpetual pall of smoke from the bottle ovens. Smog, a combination of smoke and fog, was a constant menace in those days before the Clean Air act and it was common to see bus conductors walking in front, guiding the bus with a torch. Time then, to put away our summer pastimes, including bombing our mates with a brown paper bag full of cold water, dropped from a bedroom window. Children had many leisure interests then, indoor and out, boys would spend many a happy hour sitting at the kitchen table, carefully making model planes from balsa wood, covering the framework with tissue paper and doping it. No, we didn't slip something in its drink, doping involved painting the tissue with a clear liquid which caused it to shrink tightly onto the frame.

We did more reading in nineteen forty seven, too, every child read comics like the Dandy and Beano, of course and there was always an annual in everyone's Christmas stocking.

Hanley library in Pall Mall had a childrens' section full of pre war books, full of interesting D.I.Y ideas. I remember making a crystal set (an early type of radio) using a crystal which had to be grown in a jamjar, a coil of wire wrapped round a piece of brushtail and listening to the Light programme (Radio One) using war surplus headphones. That book would be banned today, as it explained how to make fireworks, although chemists wouldn't sell me saltpetre!

We played outdoors too. The dark evenings and foggy nights made the gloomy entries even more mysterious, some of those entries, such as the one running between Market Street and Windmill Street, hadn't even got a working gaslamp, the stout wooden post mid way down the entry was a real hazard in the dark.

The dark entries giving access to the back doors of many houses were popular with courting couples, who could lean on the brickwork heated by the house fire. It was a favourite trick for us to watch a couple enter one of these entries, then two of us would quietly lift the pig-bin which stood in each street, swing it between us and throw it down the entry to scare them!

Another thing we'd do was to fill the metal drainpipe with paper and old rags then put a match to it. The draught up the spout would cause the blaze to roar like a blowlamp, startling those indoors. We'd play hide and street in the brick air raid shelters, which stood in every street in company with steel emergency water supply tanks. These street shelters were additional to the Anderson shelter in each backyard and as can be seen in this picture, were stoutly roofed in concrete and contained bunks constructed from 4x2 timbers and wiremesh.

Seen here is a street party, being held in Berkeley Street, Hanley on V.E. Day, May 8th 1945, to celebrate victory at the end of the 1939-45 war, The children are standing on the air raid shelter roof, some of the adults wear fancy dress and the street is bedecked in bunting. At one street party a dummy of Hitler, which was filled with straw, was suspended between two opposite houses and set ablaze, the rope burned through on one side and the burning dummy smashed a window. almost a case of Hitlers revenge after the war!

Children found other uses for the street shelters after the war, they were great to store scrap wood for Bonfire night, there was one dark night when a store caught fire and the brickwork of the shelter glowed red in the dark. Hallowe'en was almost unheard of then, there was nothing like the American custom of trick or treat, the Autumn festival belonged to Guy Fawkes. Huge pyres would be built on every street corner, some even appearing in the roadway, as there were few cars about just after the war.

There was an abundance of bonfire material, too, as many householders were scrapping the Victorian furniture which had served for generations and was now considered old-fashioned. Guy Fawkes night provided the perfect opportunity to get rid of an old feather bed, or a piece of lino, anything which would burn was acceptable.

Some weird figures appeared on top of the bonfires, Adolf Hitler had occupied the hot seat in 1945 and 6, but now Guys reappeared although they were likely to be wearing old uniforms. Fireworks had been readily available for the revival of Guy Fawkes day, following a ban during the wartime blackout, presumably these were pre-war stock, but they were in short supply by 1947.

Comics had preserved the memory of November the 5th; celebrations during the war years, and children were delighted to find fireworks back in the shops. The little corner shop had a window display of all kinds, ranging from the largest display box at 5/-(25p) to 'Little Demon' bangers for a ha'penny. A penny bought a banger which produced a real blast effect, someone stuck one in the lock of the little drapers' shop one year and blew it out of the door.

For two short years, all the old favourites were obtainable. There were, 'Flying Imps', a Squib which flew about at head height in a random pattern, then exploded, 'Jumping Jacks', which were a serpentine cracker, tied with red string, as the name implies these jumped around with a loud crack at each jump. 'Jack in the Box' was a cylindrical firework, containing a jumping Jack, which shot out at head height when the firework exploded.

All these exciting, but potentially dangerous fireworks, were eventually banned in the interests of safety. They were replaced by quieter, less spectacular effects, which children named "Fizzers". These were considered suitable for girls and babies, as loud cracks and bangs gave way to showers of sparks and sprays of light.

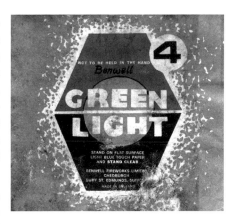

Examples include the "Green Light", manufactured by the Benwell

Company. As the name implies this emitted an emerald green flare, accompanied by a loud hiss. The "Floodlight" from long established Standard Fireworks firm, was a glaring white flame which illuminated the darkness for some distance, while the "Jackpot" imitated the Roman Candle, firing multi-coloured balls of fire into the night sky.

Repeating fireworks such as "Star Shells" and "Air Bombs" are familiar to children today, but have increased considerably in price over the years. Even as

recently as the introduction of decimal currency an enjoyable fireworks party would only cost a pound or so.

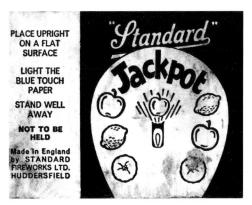

The sight of a salvo of skyrockets, bursting high in the darkness, remains one of the most popular events at firework displays and the banshee wail of the "Screecher", together with the "supersonic Bang", have their equivalents on Guy Fawkes night today.

With the growing trend towards organised displays, street corner bonfires are less

common now, but still provide an excuse for disposing of hedge clippings and similar household waste, while the cry of " Penny for the Guy" continues to echo on autumn days.

Scarcely had we re-learned the names of the various types of 'bunters', than it was November 1947 and fireworks were unobtainable. HRH Princess Elizabeth married then and fireworks were reserved for the celebrations. We'd collected material for a huge bonfire on a derelict site in the High Street, where a pottery had once stood and the Trumpet, Sea Lion and Ring o'Bells pubs were providing forms for seating and a piano accordionist. Some of the children boarded a train at Hanley station and travelled to all the towns on the Loop Line, searching for fireworks for the display, others went to Leek and Buxton without finding any. Finally, we bought some signal maroons from the Scout shop in Liverpool Road. These were six foot high rockets used as distress signals, which soared into the night sky and exploded with a deafening crack.

Photo donated

A poem recalled Hanley's pubs including 'The Angel Blew the Trumpet - Just in Time'

A road mending gang had given us some empty wooden tar barrels for the bonfire, which formed the core of the blaze, surrounded by scrap wood collected from our friend at Palmers timberyard and huge beams from the derelict potbank. The guy got a special cheer when it was placed on top of the heap, it was dressed in Grandad's moth eaten dress uniform and wore a gas mask!

When the bonfire died down we dared each other to jump over the embers, then as the pubs turned out the sky was reddened by the biggest blaze we'd seen all night. Bells clanged as the fire engines left the firestation adjacent to Webberley's to extinguish a fire in the straw stored in the packing house of a pottery - this particular factory was notorious for catching fire every Bonfire Night! It was about this time that the most popular blaze ever, occurred in Hanley, at least it was popular among the children, one afternoon as darkness fell, a huge cloud of sickly black smoke rolled over the town, visible from the highest point in Hanley, Festing Street.

We speculated about the source of the fire, which burned with multi-coloured flames, some adults remembered the time during the war when a huge bomb store exploded at Fauld. It was noticeable that there was a sweet smell to the smoke, reminiscent of burnt toffee and then we saw some of our schoolmates running up Market Street, greatly excited.

The fire was at the local sweet factory, Old Betty Plants, they told us as the fire sirens sounded all over the city. We rushed to the scene, climbing over firehoses as we crossed Broad Street to find the sweet factory well ablaze, with molten sugar and melted chocolate running in the gutter. Just as we arrived, the roof collapsed and the N. F. S firemen pulled their fire engines back in the nick of time. Crates of confectionery were piled on the pavement and the firefighters concentrated on moving these, with the assistance of what appeared to be every child in Hanley! Several cartons had been damaged, so probably some children had rather more than their sweet ration.

When all the bangs and crashes, flames and smoke had died away we were ready to start preparations for Christmas, though this was a year long event in our house. Mum would pay into a club at the grocers, the butchers and the newsagents for all the little extras. As children we knew better than to start carol singing until about a fortnight beforehand or we'd be told we were too early. Instead we restricted ourselves to writing present lists and spying out the most heavily berried holly in the hedgerows. We understood that our present list couldn't be too ambitious, with the average wage being around £5 a week. Each child would get a Christmas stocking, with a shiny 1/- (5p) in the toe, prior to 1947 silver coins were half sterling silver, later they were cupro-nickel. There would be a handful of nuts, an apple and a orange, a small toy such as a wire puzzle or a monkey up a stick, a Christmas cracker and a noisemaker with which to wake our parents early on Christmas morning. Apart from our stockings, we'd receive a compendium of board games like Ludo and snakes and ladders, with one large present to share. This seemed unfair on the only girl, who would find she had to share a train set or snooker table with her brothers.

Then there were decorations to make, sitting at the kitchen table with a bowl of flour and water paste, cutting strips of bright crepe paper, looping them together and pasting the ends to form streamers. Another type of garland was made by folding the crepe paper four times lengthways, then cutting halfway across from alternate sides, pulling the ends gave a plaited effect.

The streamers were festooned with stars, cut from the crepe paper and backed with silver paper and other colourful scraps, threaded on to cotton and draped over the streamers.

Next we turned to decorating the tree, which had to be dug up from the back garden and planted in a bucket of damp sand to take pride of place indoors over Christmas. Down came the box of fragile glass tree ornaments, a complete orchestra of gold spun glass, trumpets, bugles, drums, violins and more, all lovingly wrapped in tissue paper. There were brightly coloured birds with long feathery tails, bells, glass baubles and the fairy, who'd seen many a Christmas. Spring loaded candle holders clipped to the tree branches, miniature candles fitted, cotton wool placed at random to represent snow and sprinkled with Epsom salts for glitter. War surplus goods even figured on the tree, which was draped with ribbons of shiny silver foil backed in black. Little did we know that this was 'Window', dropped by our bombers during the war to blind enemy radar!

Having placed the Yule log, bought from a farmer felling trees in Birches Head Lane, on the hearth, we dressed to walk down Church Street for some last minute errands. The bells of St. John's rang out as we entered the Market Square, where crowds had gathered to watch Santa make his triumphal entry to Lewis's grotto, via a fire engine ladder. The seasonal displays in the shop windows were fascinating, but Santa's grotto was outstanding, having the local panto as a theme and containing numbers of illuminated tableau.

When the youngsters had received a present from Santa we returned home, where the Salvation Army band was playing under the corner gaslamp as we entered our door ready for a post war Christmas. All that was over fifty years ago and now Hanley Wakes to a new Millennium!

One of the coldest winters for years followed that Christmas, the snow which fell exceeded even that we had in 1940 and it was bitterly cold with gales driving more snow for days.

Delivering papers around Northwood Park, I was able to stand on a snowdrift and reach up to a 'phonewire, bowed down with snow and icicles. Where the snow

In the bleak mid-winter a lone shopper struggles in the snow

had drifted it reached the crossbars on the street lamps, some houses on my route down Mynors Street had a high flight of steps to the door, which had vanished beneath the snow. Many roads were almost impassable and the double decker buses, open at the rear, had difficulty climbing the steeper streets. In normal circumstances, the 'buses serving remote districts were reluctant to leave anyone. especially off the last 'bus. There was one area where the last 'bus would struggle uphill with passengers holding each other on the open platform, while others stood on the stairs, in the aisles and sitting on each others knees on the bench seats.

When a large family lived in a cosy little, two up, two down terraced house an established routine had to be followed or chaos ensued. Cold winter evenings would find us gathered in the warm kitchen, with a blazing coal fire in the deep firebasket, imagining

Bucknall Road is deserted as the snowfall freezes

faces and shapes forming in the embers.

There was just enough seating for us all, provided the youngest was on Mums' lap. Two lucky children would occupy seats at the ends of the hearth, sitting comfortably on the padded tops of the log boxes, toasting their toes on the brass fender and slices of dark rationed bread before the fire. The adults sat in armchairs, which had adjustable backrests, enabling the chairs to form a daybed.

Removing the round bolster from the chaise-longue, (settee to us), enabled the rest of the family to sit comfortably on the horse-hair stuffing, which was upholstered in black leathercloth.

The wireless would be tuned to the Light programme, where comedy or variety shows were broadcast. We all enjoyed I. T. M. A (it's that man again), starring Tommy Handley, other favourites included Up the Pole, with Jimmy Jewel and Much-binding-in -the -Marsh, featuring Kenneth Horne. Wilfred Pickles, with his 'Have a Go' quiz show was not to be missed, his catchphrases were "Are yer courtin"? and "What's on the table, Mabel".

If the accumulator which powered the wireless was discharged,

Photograph courtesy of the Potteries Museum and Art Gallery

A typical gas lit kitchen with washing hanging on the clothes rack over the leaded firegate

we'd wind up the gramophone, an H.M.V (His Masters' Voice) model, bought from Sherwins in the High Street. The gramophone was a treasured possession, gleaming in walnut veneer, with doors which opened to control the volume. A handle on the side wound the clockwork which powered the turntable, the records played at 78 rpm and if the spring ran down some amusing sound effects resulted. Inserting a steel needle into the playing arm and carefully lowering it onto the record, which was easily scratched, we'd hear the voices of Joseph Locke or Gracie Fields.

We might read comics, there was a good store in the log boxes as each child in the street would buy a different comic, swap with other children and then save them to read again.

I recall that the 'Eagle' comic appeared about then and the adventures of Dan Dare, and the green faced Treens made a pleasant change from the 'Dandy' or the 'Beano'.

As bedtime neared, the cast iron oven shelves were carefully wrapped in pieces of old blanket and taken upstairs to warm the beds, the fire would be allowed to burn low and mother would make

In this view of Hanley Market the ornate gates have closed forever, Sherwins have sold their last 78rpm record and The Grapes pub has been demolished

mugs of 'Bournville' cocoa. Supper was a couple of rich tea or digestive biscuits each, from a seven pound tin which would later serve as a bread bin.

Supper over and the dishes done, the fire would be allowed to die out, the woven mesh fireguard placed before the hearth and while dad chopped sticks and filled two buckets of coal for next morning, we'd follow mum upstairs, where a little paraffin Tilley nightlight burned by each bed.

Each bedroom had a blackleaded, cast iron firegrate, where a glowing fire was banked with coal slack to burn through the night. Frost shone on the inside of the sash windows as we climbed onto our feather beds and snuggled under the eider downs, insulated from the winter cold.

Early next morning we'd hear Dad raking the ashes from the kitchen grate, laying the fire and filling the water tank, with its polished brass tap, which formed one side of the kitchen range, providing hot water to supplement the gas boiler in the back kitchen. Then dad would fill a lidded white enamel bucket from the cold tap in the kitchen, placing it in the hearth to air and replenish the water tank. Finally, he'd bring Mum a cup of tea, before donning his pit clothes, picking up his snapping tin and leaving for work.

Chapter Six

Transformation

Homes of this type incorporating Gothic features had been erected for the master potters of the district, this particular one stood on one of the highest hills in Hanley, commanding fine views over Joiners Wharf, the Trent and the fields of Berryhill. It was to fall in the name of progress, being demolished for road widening. As the inexorable march of progress continued, more of the grand old buildings of Hanley disappeared before the bulldozers, including many fine old houses similar to the one shown, part of the history of the town was lost forever. A large detached property of this size, with several bedrooms and reception rooms, might have been converted into accommodation for two or more families and a valuable example of local architecture preserved.

A similar fate awaited many of the shops and places of entertainment which formed the town centre until well into the 1960's. Early casualties were St. John's school which stood in Lichfield Street, the Methodist school and the fine old rectory which flanked Old Hall Street, where at least a token effort was made to preserve some of the mature shrubs and trees in the grounds, an old weeping specimen being transplanted to a City park. Today, this site is occupied by Hanley 'bus station , a multi-storey carpark and Blackburn House, home of the tax inspector.

At the same time, a vendetta was continuing in the High Street against the traditional watering holes of Hanley, the Grapes, on the corner of Market Street and its neighbour, the Angel have already disappeared from the scene. On the left, the Sea Lion has gone, while the splendid old market is about to come under the hammer. Derricots' fish and chip shop, where generations enjoyed the crisp brown battered fish has closed and St. John's church stands awaiting the attentions of fly posters.

Thankfully, the Friends of St. John's are making efforts today to ensure the survival of this, one of Hanley's oldest surviving buildings. Partially concealed by the church, three high rise blocks of flats are nearing completion, providing a grandstand view of the disintegration of Hanley.

More and more of the streets of old Hanley vanished forever as the heart was torn out of communities which had thrived for generations, the town centre vibrated to the thud of piledrivers as foundations and supports were constructed for the new generation of buildings which appeared in Bethesda Street, John Street, Warner Street and the surrounding area.

The tower block of Unity House, now standing derelict in turn, the award winning City Museum and Art Gallery on the site of the former Bell pottery, a new Library, police and fire stations replaced the treasured homes of the Potters.

For some years after all the demolition, large tracts lay empty in the City Centre, as illustrated by this picture of a young lady in her Sunday best, standing on the site where Unity House will one day arise. The building to the right is the Highgate 'pub, directly behind the girl is the schoolroom of the lovely Bethesda chapel, with the wall surrounding the chapel graveyard to the left, Hanley town hall is central, while a furniture van waits on the vacant ground to remove the contents of the remaining houses.

The area around Bethesday Street in the 1950's - compare with the scene today on page 87

When this was nearly completed the empty plots of land served as free carparks, after the City centre workers had gone home, the side streets in this part of Hanley were deserted in the evening, scattered gaslamps gave an eerie atmosphere.

This pleasant 'detached' house remained in solitary splendour at the corner of Warner Street and Cannon Street, where it had served successive generations and waited its turn to fall. In the meantime the light in the parlour was like a beacon, attracting motorists in distress to approach the householder with requests for assistance or permission to use the toilet. Such callers appeared quite surprised when he objected, being under the impression that he was an attendant for the car park!

By this time, most of the older part of Hanley's housing in the central area had been demolished and the occupants dispersed to vast new estates of council houses, far from town and on farmland on the outskirts of the City. A typical estate at that time was built at Bentilee and a letter written then reads'

This 1950's picture of a house on the eventual site of Unity House - contrast with the picture on page 88

"As the estate and the satellites at Ubberley and Berryhill were completed, people from all over Stoke-on-Trent and the North of England came to live there. The only 'bus service was from Hanley to Twigg Street, the roads leading to homes were covered in slimy marl. How the furniture removal vans managed to negotiate the roads was marvellous. There was another 'bus route, enabling travel via Ash Bank to Hanley, Leek and Cheadle, but this could only be reached by crossing two fields and wading a brook. At that date, the fare from Hanley to Twigg Street was threepence ha'penny!

Eventually, better lighting was introduced to replace the original and many of the new residents became involved in the work of establishing workingmens' clubs, such as the Ubberley and Bentilee

Slimy 'marl' finally produced prize-winning hybrid tea roses like these after years of hard work

and the Auto, which was later converted into a supermarket. Breweries set up several pubs, the Beverley and Man o' Clay among them, together with a community hall, originally in the old Co-Op and followed by a purpose built community hall, named for Sir Harold Clowes who was largely instrumental in the fund raising".

Despite the original difficulties, the new tenants found the stiff clay soil produced some magnificent rose gardens.

New homes were being erected on some of the sites left empty by demolition, the shops once occupied by the 'Penny-pop man', the tinware shop and the Chinese laundry being replaced by a new estate, including six high rise apartment blocks. A footbridge linked the opposite sides of the estate across Bucknall New Road, the architect incorporating the linear curve of a rugby ball into the shape of the supporting arches.

Seen in the view above are the rising platforms being used to fit new uPVC double glazed picture windows to Lindop Court, the picture apparently having been shot from neighbouring Seddon Court.

Chapter 7

Full Circle

What a contrast in comparing this picture with that in the previous chapter,which shows a young girl standing before an empty lot in Hanley City centre. Where rows of cosy little terrace homes once stood, there are now the grounds of the Library in Bethesda Street, in the right foreground, while a grove of mature silver birches screens the City Museum to the left. The schoolrooms forming part of the Bethesda Church dominate the centre of this picture,having recently been adapted for commercial purposes, while the exterior of the beautiful old Church has been allowed to fall into disrepair.

One corner of Bethesda Church frames the left of this scene, with Hanley Town Hall,Blackburn House and the original fabric of the recently refurbished Victoria Hall beyond. The newly completed entrance to the Victoria Hall is just visible on the right, with the new brickwork in contrast to the surrounding buildings.

Hanley Wakes

A comparison between this recent picture of the now derelict Unity House and the little home shown on the same site in the previous chapter, illustrates the changes which have taken place in the City Centre during the years described in this book.Large areas of Hanley are now dedicated as car parks, that at Hinde Street appears at the left in this picture and parking locally is becoming prohibitively expensive. In recent years proposals

Terraced houses . .to tower block . .to Casino?

for this building have included suggestions that it should be converted into flats, used to house the homeless and most recently, that the building be demolished for a supermarket to be erected on the site.

After serving as the administrative centre used by the Council for several years, Unity House has been abandoned in favour of a luxurious new Civic Centre built in Stoke.

One building in Hanley City Centre which has changed little in external appearance is 'The Foyer', the former entrance to the Odeon cinema,previously known as the Grand Theatre, before a disastrous fire. Much of the Art Deco style of architecture which distinguished an Odeon cinema remains, the tile cladding covering the distinctive

curved frontage having been cleaned and renovated, this photo differs little from that which appears in the first chapter of this book.

Apart from the new name in lights and the addition of extra spotlights, a new paint job on the entrance arch and other cosmetic touches, any former cinema patron would recognise the spot where the queue would form for the one and nines to see such long running features as 'South Pacific', 'The Sound of Music' and 'Bedknobs and Broomsticks'.

Pass through the entry doors, however, and the cashiers' desk has disappeared, together with the kiosk selling sweets, chocolate and tobacco.

The staircase no longer leads to plush seats in the circle, nor will an usherette with her torch offer ice-cream or drinks on a stick. Instead, a luxurious bar and dining area provide the setting for a meal or a drink, while the main body of the cinema is being re-modelled.

Walking through the arcade which replaced the Empire cinema, then to the junction of Piccadilly and Pall Mall, the Regent cinema, (a.k.a) the Gaumont has reverted to The Regent theatre as part of the general refurbishment of the City Centre. In the interval since the photo in Chapter one was taken, The Regent has been considerably extended and improved to include facilities for staging the latest shows. New street furniture has appeared, seating, street lights and - unheard of when the original picture was taken - C.C.T.V. cameras on a stick. Piccadilly itself has been pedestrianised, although at the time of writing, motorists have difficulty in adapting to this. The sports shop adjoining The Regent, which sold fishing gear, including the ground

Now and then. Pall Mall viewed from Picadilly today and as it was in 1947 on page 20.

bait catapults which we used to good effect as schoolboys, has gone and the corner shop where we would spend our sweet ration coupons has become a snackbar.

Hanley town hall, seen at the top of this scene, is being enhanced by the construction of a new approach, the area surrounding the Cenotaph is now paved and mature trees have been planted, illuminated by concealed floodlights.

Crossing Lichfield Street by the Albion Hotel, we approach Hanley 'bus station, overshadowd by a derelict footbridge from the multi-storey car park. The bulk of Blackburn House looms over what is considered by many to be one of the coldest, draughtiest and

Red and Yellow PMT buses mingle with the new colours of First'Bus in this picture of Hanley 'bus Station and the store now used by BM

most comfortless bus stations known. However, all this area is about to be demolished in its turn, Wilkinsons' store has moved to the former C and A shop in Stafford Street and many buildings in Charles Street may soon bite the dust!

This magnificent Weeping Willow now graces the site of the high rise apartments seen in the previous chapter. Groves of Alders and other mature plantings

grow on this site, where the high buildings provide splendid views over the City.

The C.C.T.V cameras which have recently appeared on some of these blocks, enable the traffic flow on the ring road and around the City Centre to be monitored, while contributing to the general security of this estate. Seen on the right of the picture on the previous page, are the distinctive arched supports of the footbridge which links the seperate halves of the estate and spans Bucknall Road. This footbridge offers an unrivalled viewpoint to observe the passing scene, on the eve of the Millennium it was crowded by children watching the fireworks across the eastern area of the City.

Many other events have passed under this bridge, including an open topped 'bus bearing Stoke City players and officials following their last cup run.

The school railings are dressed with the colours of Stoke City F.C. as the children bid farewell

Most poignant of all was a sad event, the final visit by the funeral cortege of Sir Stanley Matthews to his old school, St.Luke's. A section of the crowds who lined Bucknall Road are shown here as the procession pauses, en route to the City Centre on a cold gray March day. And now the wheels of time have turned full circle,some aspects of Hanley have scarcely changed,while others have altered beyond recognition - who knows which was the better?

Hanley Wakes

Hanley Wakes